First Mental Arithmetic 5

Answers

Ann Montague-Smith

Schofield & Sims

Teacher's notes

The format of *First Mental Arithmetic* differs from that of traditional mental arithmetic materials in that the children read the questions themselves and write down their answers. The individual books may be used flexibly and children may set their own pace. However, you might find it helpful to use one book per term.

The mathematical content of the *First Mental Arithmetic* activities should already have been covered in maths lessons and the reading content is kept simple. Nevertheless, you might consider asking a classroom assistant to work with a group of children, helping them to read the questions. Ask the assistant to note the names of children needing further help, and the activities or concepts that they find difficult. You can then provide the necessary teaching, support or additional practice.

Books 4 to 6

Books 4 to 6 are designed for Year 2 but are also suitable for some older children. Each book is split into three sections. The sections are divided into sessions, each comprising one page of 30 questions. Parts A, B and C of each session contain different question types; for further details, please see the back cover. Depending on the child's skills, a session's work may be completed during the course of a week or over whatever time span you feel is appropriate.

As the children progress, different levels of support are provided. By the time they reach Books 4 to 6, the children will know some key maths facts. If they cannot recall these, they should be aware of strategies that will help them to find answers. Children needing more help may find a number line useful – either an actual line or one that they visualise.

Encourage the children to use the following mental strategies when working through Book 5.

- For addition and subtraction: using known facts to help them to find the answer. (For example, from $6 + 3 = 9$, they can work out that $36 + 3 = 39$; from $9 - 4 = 5$, they can deduce that $9 - 5 = 4$.)
- For finding the difference: counting up from the smaller to the larger number. (For example, for the difference between 19 and 21, they count up, 19 to 20, then one more to 21.)
- For multiplication: knowing the basic multiplication facts.
- For division: recognising that if they know $5 \times 2 = 10$, they can deduce that $10 \div 2 = 5$ and $10 \div 5 = 2$.
- For fractions: using squared paper to model the problem. (For example, for finding ¾ of 12, they would mark out a grid of 12 squares, find ½, then find ¼ or ½ of ½, then find ¾.)

Assessment

- The check-ups at the end of each section test all the concepts and facts covered in that section.
- An additional test checks children's understanding of *Shape and space* and *Handling data*.
- As children write their answers to the *Just facts* tests, they will notice helpful patterns. *Just facts* in Book 5 covers doubles to 20, pairs that make 20 and multiplication facts for 2s, 5s and 10s.

Record keeping

At the beginning of each workbook section is a photocopiable *Achievement chart* for completion by the child. In this book of answers, the *Achievement charts* are replaced by photocopiable *Group record sheets*, which allow you to note problem areas for each child. For example, you might write: *Knows multiplication facts for 2* or *Needs practice in writing number family facts*. Alternatively, you can simply record the child's marks. Use the completed sheets to plan appropriate work.

Children who have successfully completed *First Mental Arithmetic Book 5* may move on to *First Mental Arithmetic Book 6*, obtainable separately from Schofield & Sims.

Contents

Section 1 Group record sheet

Class _____

Name	Read and write numbers to 1000 in figures and words Session 1	Know which are odd and which are even numbers Session 1	Know what each digit in a two-digit number stands for Session 1	Partition numbers in different ways Session 3	Doubles to 20 Session 3	Recall number facts for each number to 10 Session 4	Add and subtract mentally Session 5

From: **First Mental Arithmetic 5 Answers** by Ann Montague-Smith (ISBN 978 07217 1173 7). Copyright © Schofield & Sims Ltd, 2011. Published by Schofield & Sims Ltd, Dogley Mill, Fenay Bridge, Huddersfield HD8 0NQ, UK (www.schofieldandsims.co.uk). This page may be photocopied for use within your school or institution only.

Section 1 Session 1

Session Focus
Read and write numbers to 1000 in figures and words
Know which are odd and which are even numbers
Know what each digit in a two-digit number stands for

A   ANSWER

1
| H | T | U |
| 1 | 3 | 2 | is `132`

2
| H | T | U |
| 2 | 3 | 1 | is `231`

132 231 213 312 321 324

3 Which are the odd numbers?
`231` `213` `321`

4 Which are the even numbers?
`132` `312` `324`

5 Write eighteen in numbers. `18`

6 Make two-digit numbers from **3** and **4**.
`34` and `43`

7 Which two digits do **45** and **54** use?
`4` and `5`

8 Write **123** in words.
`one hundred and twenty-three`

9 Write three hundred and thirty-six in figures. `336`

10 Write four hundred and nine in figures. `409`

B   ANSWER

1 Write the number that has four hundreds, three tens and seven units. `437`

2 Write the number that has six hundreds, seven tens and eight units. `678`

3 Write **492** in words.
`four hundred and ninety-two`

4 Is three hundred and sixty-one odd or even? `odd`

5 Is five hundred and thirty-two odd or even? `even`

6 Partition twenty-six into tens and units.
`2` tens and `6` units.

7 How many tens in **94**? `9`

8 How many units in **70**? `0`

9 Write the number that has six hundreds, seven tens and eight units. `678`

10 Write **490** in words.
`four hundred and ninety`

C   ANSWER

1 Write two odd numbers using **3 6 4**. `643` and `463`

2 Write two even numbers using **3 6 7**. `376` and `736`

3 Write the number that is **1** more than **123**. `124`

4 Write the number that is **1** less than **647**. `646`

5 Write one thousand in figures. `1000`

6 Write the next even number after **234**. `236`

7 Write the next odd number after **757**. `759`

8 Write ninety-two as
`9` tens and `2` units.

9 Write seventy-seven as
`7` tens and `7` units.

10 Write **647** in words.
`six hundred and forty-seven`

5

Section 1　Session 2

Session Focus
Read and write numbers to 1000 in figures and words
Know which are odd and which even numbers
Know what each digit in a two-digit number stands for

A　　　　　　　　　　ANSWER

1 Write one hundred and sixty-two in figures.　`162`

2 Write three hundred and forty-five in figures.　`345`

3 Write **21** in words.　`twenty-one`

4 Write **101** in words.
`one hundred and one`

5 Is **564** odd or even?　`even`

6 Is nine hundred and ninety one odd or even?　`odd`

7 Use **1**, **2**, **3** to make an even number.　`132` or `312`

8 Write **5** tens and **4** units as a two-digit number.　`54`

9 Write **63** as
`6` tens and `3` units.

10 Write **40** as
`4` tens and `0` units.

B　　　　　　　　　　ANSWER

1 **40 + 2** = `42`

2 **90 + 3** = `93`

3 **70 + 6** = `76`

4 **20 + 0** = `20`

5 **10 + 10 + 4** = `24`

6 Write **769** in words.
`seven hundred and sixty-nine`

7 Write nine hundred and one in figures.　`901`

8 Make two different odd numbers from **4**, **5** and **6**.　`465` and `645`

9 Make two different even numbers from **7**, **8** and **9**.　`798` and `978`

10 Make two even numbers from **0**, **3** and **7**.　`370` and `730`

C　　　　　　　　　　ANSWER

1 Write 6 three-digit numbers from **1**, **3** and **5**.　`135` `153` `315` `351` `513` `531`

2 Write 6 three-digit numbers from **2**, **4** and **6**.　`246` `264` `426` `462` `624` `642`

3 Ten plus ten plus ten plus five is　`35`

4 Ten plus ten plus ten plus one plus three is　`34`

5 **70 + 10 + 10 + 4 + 1 =**　`95`

6 Write an odd number between **34** and **36**.　`35`

7 Write an even number between **67** and **69**.　`68`

8 Is three hundred and sixty-five odd or even?　`odd`

9 Is one thousand odd or even?　`even`

10 Write one thousand as
`1` thousands `0` hundreds
`0` tens `0` units.

Section 1   Session 3

A | ANSWER

1	10 + 10 + 10 + 3	=	33
2	50 + 10 + 4 + 2	=	66
3	60 + 10 + 1 + 1 + 3	=	75
4	11 + 11	=	22
5	12 + 12	=	24
6	15 + 15	=	30
7	20 + 20	=	40
8	13 + 13	=	26
9	16 + 16	=	32
10	18 + 18	=	36

B | ANSWER

1 Partition **36** into

   3 tens and 6 units.

2 Forty-eight can be written as

   4 tens and 8 units.

3	Double **14** is	28
4	Double **19** is	38
5	Double **16** is	32
6	Double **12** is	24
7	Double **15** is	30
8	Double **17** is	34
9	Double **10** is	20
10	Double **20** is	40

C | ANSWER

1 Write six numbers using the digits

   6, **7** and **8**. | 678 | 687 | 768 |
                                | 786 | 867 | 876 |

2 What is the next number after
   nine hundred and ninety-nine?

   one thousand

3 What number has
   three hundreds and
   no tens and no units?   300

Tom	*15*
Bill	*18*
Liz	*20*
Peter	*14*

4 Tom doubles his score.
   What is his score now?   30

5 Bill doubles his score.
   What is his score now?   36

6 Liz doubles her score.
   What is her score now?   40

7 Peter doubles his score.
   What is his score now?   28

8 Two baskets each have
   19 eggs in them. How many
   eggs is that in total?   38

9 There are two trays of
   15 cakes. How many cakes
   are there altogether?   30

10 There are two litters of
    11 puppies. How many
    puppies are there in total?   22

Section 1 Session 4

Session Focus
Recall number facts for each number to 10
Doubles to 20

A | ANSWER

1	7 + 4	=	11
2	6 + 5	=	11
3	8 + 4	=	12
4	12 – 3	=	9
5	19 – 9	=	10
6	11 + 11	=	22
7	14 + 14	=	28
8	19 + 19	=	38
9	13 + 13	=	26
10	12 + 12	=	24

B | ANSWER

1	6 + ▢ = 13	7
2	▢ + 4 = 14	10
3	▢ – 3 = 12	15
4	17 – ▢ = 9	8
5	12 – 10 = ▢	2
6	Double 18 is	36
7	Double 16 is	32
8	Double 20 is	40
9	Double 15 is	30
10	Double 17 is	34

C | ANSWER

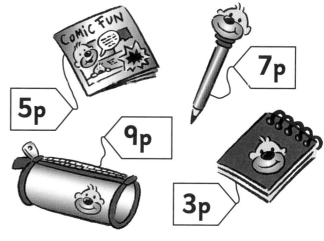

How much do these cost?

1	a pencil and a comic?	12p
2	a pencil case and a comic?	14p

How much change from **20p** if you buy

3	a pencil case?	11p
4	a pencil?	13p
5	a comic and a notepad?	12p
6	Marbles come in bags of **12**. How many marbles are there in two bags?	24
7	The farmer has **14** ducklings and **14** chicks. How many birds is that altogether?	28
8	Pears are sold in bags of **15**. How many pears are there in two bags?	30
9	There are **17** sheep and **17** cows. How many animals are there in total?	34
10	**19** cows and **19** pigs go to market. How many animals is that?	38

Section 1   Session 5

A | ANSWER

1	50 + 9	=	59
2	32 + 6	=	38
3	46 + 5	=	51
4	62 – 2	=	60
5	72 – 3	=	69
6	15 + 15	=	30
7	17 + 17	=	34
8	12 + 12	=	24
9	16 + 16	=	32
10	18 + 18	=	36

B | ANSWER

1	56 add 5 is	61
2	34 and 8 is	42
3	92 subtract 4 is	88
4	54 minus 7 is	47
5	26 add 7 equals	33
6	Double 11 is	22
7	Double 19 is	38
8	Double 13 is	26
9	Double 20 is	40
10	Double 15 is	30

C | ANSWER

1	Tom has **52** stickers. His mum gives him another **9** stickers. How many stickers does Tom have in total?	61
2	Mair and Jacinta have **15** beads each. How many do they have altogether?	30
3	Paul has **54kg** of potatoes. He sells **6kg**. How many kg are left?	48kg
4	Sam buys **2** sacks of carrots. Each sack weighs **17kg**. How much is that in total?	34kg
5	Sahil counts out **39** biscuits onto a plate. Mark eats **7** of the biscuits. How many are left?	32
6	Tom has **18** points. He doubles his score. What is his score now?	36
7	Pam counts **45** sheep in the field. The farmer puts **2** more sheep into the field. How many sheep are there in total?	47
8	**14** starlings are on the lawn. Another **14** starlings come to the lawn. How many starlings is that in total?	28
9	**47** beads are dropped onto the floor. All but **9** are picked up. How many beads are picked up?	38
10	**16** dogs and **16** cats live at the pet sanctuary. How many animals is that altogether?	32

9

Section 1   Session 6

Session Focus
Add and subtract mentally
Recall number facts for each number to 10

A | ANSWER

1	64 – 5	=	59
2	92 – 4	=	88
3	32 + 8	=	40
4	46 + 5	=	51
5	34 – 6	=	28
6	9 + 4	=	13
7	8 + 5	=	13
8	16 – 12	=	4
9	19 – 4	=	15
10	20 – 10	=	10

B | ANSWER

1	Forty-six add seven is	fifty-three
2	Eighty-eight add eight is	ninety-six
3	Twenty-six subtract seven is	nineteen
4	Thirty-seven and four makes	forty-one
5	Fifty-one take away three leaves	forty-eight
6	19 – ___ = 12	7
7	___ – 2 = 15	17
8	3 + ___ = 12	9
9	6 + ___ = 17	11
10	19 – ___ = 8	11

C | ANSWER

45   17   64   32   90

1	The farmer sends **6** of the cows to market. How many cows are left on the farm?	39
2	Another **8** pigs are born. How many pigs are there now?	40
3	**5** of the sheep have lambs. How many sheep do not have lambs?	59
4	**5** horses are sold. How many horses are left?	85
5	The farmer buys another **8** goats. How many goats are there now?	25
6	There are **4** ponies and **8** donkies at another farm. How many animals is that in total?	12
7	The chickens lay **7** eggs on Monday and **8** eggs on Tuesday. How many eggs is that?	15
8	**9** ducks fly away and **1** duck is left on the pond. How many ducks were there to start with?	10
9	There are **8** goldfish and **6** cream fish in the pond. How many fish are there altogether?	14
10	**11** chickens live in the hen house. **7** chickens go to market. How many chickens are left?	4

Section 1 Session 7

Session Focus
Add and subtract mentally
Recall number facts for each number to 10

A   ANSWER

1	54 + 3	=	57
2	67 + 5	=	72
3	31 − 4	=	27
4	43 − 7	=	36
5	56 + 4	=	60
6	9 + 2	=	11
7	7 + 5	=	12
8	9 + 6	=	15
9	18 − 7	=	11
10	16 − 9	=	7

B   ANSWER

1	58 add 4 equals	62
2	43 subtract 5 is	38
3	21 minus 8 is	13
4	23 add 7 is	30
5	32 take away 3 is	29
6	The difference between 17 and 3 is	14
7	9 add 3 equals	12
8	13 minus 4 is	9
9	14 subtract 4 is	10
10	2 and 9 is	11

C   ANSWER

The prices in the shop have changed.

Write the correct price onto each label.

1	~~45p~~ + 6p	51p
2	~~62p~~ − 4p	58p
3	~~54p~~ + 2p	56p
4	~~97p~~ + 3p	£1 or 100p
5	~~38p~~ −10p	28p

6	Paul has **15p**. He spends **9p**. What is his change?	6p
7	Sam has **11p**. She spends **5p**. How much money does she have left?	6p
8	Mark has **9p**. His mum gives him **2p**. How much money does he have now?	11p
9	Gina has **12p**. She spends **3p**. How much change does she get?	9p
10	Mairhi has **7p**. She spends **7p**. How much money does she have now?	0p

Section 1 Session 8

Session Focus
Add and subtract mentally
Recall number facts for each number to 10

A
			ANSWER
1	52 – 3	=	49
2	49 + 6	=	55
3	32 – 4	=	28
4	45 + 5	=	50
5	76 – 8	=	68
6	4 + 9	=	13
7	17 – 2	=	15
8	18 – 8	=	10
9	5 + 7	=	12
10	15 – 8	=	7

B
		ANSWER
1	___ + 2 = 48	46
2	71 – ___ = 69	2
3	43 + ___ = 50	7
4	99 + ___ = 100	1
5	___ – 7 = 70	77
6	___ + 9 = 12	3
7	11 – ___ = 5	6
8	8 + ___ = 8	0
9	___ – 7 = 5	12
10	___ + 2 = 11	9

C
		ANSWER
1	There are **29** blue pens and **4** red ones. How many pens are there in total?	33
2	There are **45** books on the shelf. The librarian puts another **6** books on the shelf. How many books are there in total?	51
3	**46** sheep are in the field. **6** of the sheep go into the shelter. How many sheep are left in the field?	40
4	**17** cows are in the milking parlour. **8** cows go back to the field. How many cows are left in the milking parlour?	9
5	**29** cars wait at the traffic lights. Only **4** cars go through the lights. How many cars are still at the traffic lights?	25

Here is Paul's homework.

Tick the answers that are correct.

Write the correct number sentence where the answer is wrong.

6	**7 + 4 = 11**	✓	
7	**5 + 6 = 8**		5 + 6 = 11
8	**14 – 5 = 6**		14 – 5 = 9
9	**8 + 6 = 10**		8 + 6 = 14
10	**9 + 5 = 14**	✓	

Section 1   Session 9

A   ANSWER

1   **4** tens and **3** units is   `43`

2   **96** can be written as
    `9` tens and `6` units.

3   **70** can be written as
    `7` tens and `0` units.

4   **6** tens and **3** units is   `63`

5   **10** tens can be written as   `100`

6   **15 + 15 =**   `30`

7   **19 + 19 =**   `38`

8   **13 + 13 =**   `26`

9   **16 + 16 =**   `32`

10 **14 + 14 =**   `28`

B   ANSWER

1   What number is the same as
    4 tens and **3** units?   `43`

2   What number can be written as
    10 + 10 + 10 + 1?   `31`

3   4 `6` is the same as
    `4` tens and **6** units.

4   **96** is the same as
    `9` tens and `6` units.

5   `2` 7 is the same as
    2 tens and `7` units.

6   Double **11** is   `22`

7   Double **12** is   `24`

8   Double **20** is   `40`

9   Double **18** is   `36`

10 Double **17** is   `34`

C   ANSWER

1   How many tens are there
    in **57**?   `5`

2   How many units are there
    in **82**?   `2`

3   **10 + 20 + 10 + 1 + 3 + 2 =**   `46`

4   **50 + 20 + 10 + 3 + 5   =**   `88`

5   **20 + 20 + 30 + 5 + 5   =**   `80`

6   Mark scored double **18**.
    How many is that?   `36`

7   Tamwar scored double **11**.
    How many did he score?   `22`

8   Phil scored double **13**.
    How many points did he win?   `26`

9   Jill scored double **20**.
    How many is that?   `40`

10 Sally scored double **15**.
    How many points did she win?   `30`

Section 1 Session 10

Session Focus
Doubles to 20
Add and subtract mentally
Recall number facts for each number to 10

A

			ANSWER
1	16 + 16	=	32
2	14 + 14	=	28
3	19 + 19	=	38
4	12 + 12	=	24
5	19 + 6	=	25
6	44 – 5	=	39
7	32 + 9	=	41
8	6 + 7	=	13
9	11 – 4	=	7
10	15 – 6	=	9

B

		ANSWER
1	Double **11** is	22
2	Double **20** is	40
3	Double **18** is	36
4	☐ + 4 = 50	46
5	36 + ☐ = 40	4
6	45 – ☐ = 38	7
7	☐ – 5 = 39	44
8	The difference between **17** and **9** is	8
9	**15** minus ☐ is **9**.	6
10	☐ and **8** is **13**.	5

C

		ANSWER
1	Paul has **14** marbles. Jim has twice as many. How many marbles does Jim have?	28
2	Jill has **18** stickers. Mary has twice as many. How many stickers does Mary have?	36
3	Jon has **15** stamps and so does Sid. How many stamps do Jon and Sid have in total?	30
4	There are **20** ducks and **20** hens. How many birds are there in total?	40
5	Paul has **46** stamps. How many more does he need to make **50**?	4
6	Sara has **92** beads. How many more does she need so that she has **100**?	8
7	Jon makes **32** biscuits. He eats **3** of them. How many biscuits are there now?	29
8	**14** dogs are playing in the park. **5** go home. How many are left in the park?	9
9	**7** sparrows eat breadcrumbs. **5** sparrows do not eat the crumbs. How many sparrows are there in total?	12
10	There are **7** children playing football. **9** children watch the game. How many children are there altogether?	16

Section 1 Check-up 1

1   ANSWER

1 Write **563** in words.

five hundred and sixty-three

2 Write nine hundred and sixty-four in figures. → 964

3 Write the odd number.

631 526 910 → 631

4 Write the even number.

545 554 455 → 554

5 9 | 3 | is the same as

| 9 | tens and **3** units.

6 **96** is the same as

50 + | 40 | + 4 + | 2 |

7 Double **14** is → 28

8 Double **19** is → 38

9 Double **13** is → 26

10 **62 + 7** = → 69

11 **31 – 4** = → 27

12 **36 + 5** = → 41

13 **9 + 7** = → 16

14 **7 + 6** = → 13

15 **8 + 4** = → 12

16 Write nine hundred and seven in figures. → 907

17 Write **407** in words.

four hundred and seven

18 Write the next odd number after **334**. → 335

19 Write the even number just before **333**. → 332

20 | 4 | **7** is the same as

4 tens and | 7 | units.

21 **10 + 20 + 30 + 4 + 2 =** → 66

22 Mark has two bags of **17** marbles. How many marbles is that altogether? → 34

23 Tom has **12** apples and **12** oranges. How many pieces of fruit is that in total? → 24

24 There are **42** cakes. Pat eats **3** cakes. How many cakes are left? → 39

25 Sally puts **42** pink iced cakes and **7** white iced cakes on a tray. How many cakes is that in total? → 49

26 Pavil has **7** cats and **5** dogs. How many pets does he have? → 12

27 **13** birds sit on the roof. **5** birds fly away. How many birds are left on the roof? → 8

28 **9** black pencils and **4** red pencils are in the pencil case. How many pencils is that in total? → 13

29 There are **6** sparrows and **8** finches by the bird table. How many birds is that altogether? → 14

30 **15** starlings are on the lawn. **6** starlings fly away. How many birds are left? → 9

Section 2   Group record sheet

Class _____

Name Session 1	Add and subtract mentally Session 1	Recall number facts for each number to 10 Session 1	Know pairs that total 20 Session 2	Missing number sequences Session 4	Multiplication facts for 2s, 5s and 10s Session 5	Sharing Session 7	Doubles to 20 Session 7

From: **First Mental Arithmetic 5 Answers** by Ann Montague-Smith (ISBN 978 07217 1173 7). Copyright © Schofield & Sims Ltd, 2011. Published by Schofield & Sims Ltd, Dogley Mill, Fenay Bridge, Huddersfield HD8 0NQ, UK (www.schofieldandsims.co.uk). This page may be photocopied for use within your school or institution only.

Section 2   Session 1

Session Focus
Add and subtract mentally
Recall number facts for each number to 10

A   ANSWER

1   **23 + 6**   =   29

2   **42 – 3**   =   39

3   **34 + 6**   =   40

4   **35 – 7**   =   28

5   **29 + 7**   =   36

6   **9 + 4**   =   13

7   **13 – 8**   =   5

8   **3 + 8**   =   11

9   **8 + 7**   =   15

10 **9 + 7**   =   16

B   ANSWER

1   **54** subtract **8** is   46

2   **36** add ▨ equals **40**.   4

3   **97** subtract ▨ leaves **90**.   7

4   ▨ add **4** is **90**.   86

5   **15** subtract **8** leaves   7

6   ▨ subtract **4** leaves **9**.   13

7   ▨ add **7** equals **14**.   7

8   **15** subtract ▨ equals **9**.   6

9   **6** add ▨ equals **15**.   9

10 ▨ add **3** is **83**.   80

C   ANSWER

1   There are **54** oranges.
    5 are sold. How many
    oranges are left?   49

2   **48** apples are in the crate.
    4 more are added. How many
    apples are there altogether?   52

3   The shop sells **28** pears. There
    are **6** pears left. How many
    pears were there to start with?   34

4   **37** mangoes are sold. There are
    4 left. How many mangoes
    were there to begin with?   41

5   The shop has **62** bananas.
    They sell **8** bananas.
    How many bananas are left?   54

Chews	9p
Mints	8p
Hearts	7p
Toffees	6p

6   How much is a pack of Chews
    and a pack of Toffees?   15p

7   How much is a pack of Hearts
    and a pack of Mints?   15p

8   Tom buys some Mints and some
    Toffees. How much change
    will he get from **20p**?   6p

9   Sally buys some Hearts and some
    Chews. How much change
    will she get from **20p**?   4p

10 What change from **20p** will
    Pat get if she buys some
    Hearts and some Toffees?   7p

Section 2   Session 2

Session Focus
Recall number facts for each number to 10
Know pairs that total 20

A

			ANSWER
1	$5 + 6$	=	11
2	$9 + 7$	=	16
3	$13 - 4$	=	9
4	$17 - 9$	=	8
5	$16 - 7$	=	9
6	$10 + 10$	=	20
7	$11 + \quad = 20$		9
8	$14 + \quad = 20$		6
9	$18 + \quad = 20$		2
10	$13 + \quad = 20$		7

B

		ANSWER
1	$6 + \quad = 15$	9
2	$9 + \quad = 13$	4
3	$\quad - 4 = 7$	11
4	$12 - \quad = 9$	3
5	$\quad + 8 = 14$	6
6	$\quad + 4 = 20$	16
7	$8 + \quad = 20$	12
8	$9 + \quad = 20$	11
9	$15 + \quad = 20$	5
10	$\quad + 10 = 20$	10

C

ANSWER

How much do you spend if you buy

1	a pencil for **9p** and a notepad for **4p**?	13p
2	a lolly for **8p** and a chew for **4p**?	12p
3	two **7p** lollies?	14p

Which coins do you choose to pay the exact amount for

4   an **8p** pen and a **7p** pencil?

  10p and 5p

5   a **3p** chew and an **8p** lolly?

  10p and 1p

20p

How much change do you get from **20p** if you buy

6	a **13p** lolly?	7p
7	an **18p** book?	2p
8	a **14p** pen?	6p
9	a **16p** CD?	4p
10	a **15p** ruler?	5p

Section 2   Session 3

Session Focus
Recall number facts for each number to 10
Know pairs that total 20

A   ANSWER

1   8 + 4   =   12

2   9 + 3   =   12

3   5 + 7   =   12

4   6 + 8   =   14

5   2 + 9   =   11

6   3 + 17   =   20

7   9 +   = 20   11

8   13 +   = 20   7

9   16 +   = 20   4

10 5 +   = 20   15

B   ANSWER

1   3 and   equals 12.   9

2   and 7 equals 15.   8

3   14 subtract   equals 8.   6

4   The difference between
    14 and 9 is   5

5   The difference between
    6 and 13 is   7

6   15 and   equals 20.   5

7   and 7 makes 20.   13

8   9 and   equals 20.   11

9   20 subtract 3 leaves   17

10 20 subtract 8 leaves   12

C   ANSWER

1   Tom has **20** marbles.
    He puts **7** of them in
    his pocket.
    How many marbles
    are not in Tom's pocket?   13

2   Sara has **20** stickers.
    She puts some of the
    stickers in the album.
    She has **8** left over.
    How many stickers did
    she put in the album?   12

3   Mark has **11** black pens and
    9 red pens. How many pens
    does Mark have in total?   20

4   There are **20** balls in the bag.
    18 balls are red. The rest are
    white. How many balls
    are white?   2

5   Anna has **20p**.
    She spends **14p**.
    How much money
    does she have left?   6p

6   Nine and seven equals   sixteen

7   Eight and nine is   seventeen

8   Six and five equals   eleven

9   The difference between
    eleven and nine is   two

10 The difference between
    twelve and four is   eight

19

Section 2 Session 4

Session Focus
Add and subtract mentally
Missing number sequences

A

		ANSWER
1	42 + 7 =	49
2	54 + 7 =	61
3	74 – 5 =	69
4	65 – 8 =	57
5	23 + 7 =	30

6 15 16 17 **18** **19** 20

7 31 32 **33** **34** 35 **36**

8 21 23 **25** **27** **29** 31

9 44 46 48 **50** **52** **54**

10 **30** **32** **34** 36 38 40

B

		ANSWER
1	54 – ___ = 46	8
2	63 – 7 = ___	56
3	84 – ___ = 76	8
4	23 + ___ = 31	8
5	54 + ___ = 62	8

What number do you land on when you

6	start at **53** and count on **5** jumps of **2**?	63
7	start at **28** and count on **6** jumps of **2**?	40
8	start at **56** and count on **4** jumps of **2**?	64
9	start at **40** and count on **7** jumps of **2**?	54
10	start at **39** and count on **8** jumps of **2**?	55

C

		ANSWER
1	There are **64** sausages in the butcher's window. He sells **6** sausages. How many are left?	58
2	James has **34** books. Sam has **29** books. How many more books does James have than Sam?	5
3	There are **29** hamburgers in the butcher's window. The butcher puts another **8** hamburgers in the window. How many hamburgers are there in total in the window?	37
4	Tom has **64p** in his pocket. He spends **7p**. How much money does Tom have left?	57p
5	May has **55p** in her purse. She spends **9p**. How much money does May have left?	46p
6	What number do you land on if you start on **46** and jump back **5** lots of **2**?	36
7	How many jumps do you make if you start on **67** and jump back in **2**s to **55**?	6
8	Zainab stands on **36**. She decides that if she makes **3** jumps of **2** she will land on **40**. Is she correct?	no
9	Atul stands on **45**. He decides that if he makes **4** jumps back of **2** he will land on **37**. Is he correct?	yes
10	Peter jumps forward **3** jumps of **2**. He lands on **36**. What number did Peter start on?	30

Section 2   Session 5

Session Focus
Multiplication facts for 2s, 5s and 10s

A | ANSWER

1	5×2	=	10
2	8×2	=	16
3	3×2	=	6
4	2×5	=	10
5	8×2	=	16
6	6×5	=	30
7	2×10	=	20
8	7×10	=	70
9	9×10	=	90
10	4×10	=	40

B | ANSWER

1	$ \times 5 = 40$	8
2	$ \times 2 = 18$	9
3	$ \times 10 = 60$	6
4	$4 \times = 20$	5
5	$3 \times = 30$	10
6	$7 \times = 35$	5
7	$ \times 5 = 45$	9
8	$ \times 10 = 50$	5
9	$ \times 2 = 14$	7
10	$ \times 5 = 25$	5

C | ANSWER

8 beads   **9** marbles

6 counters

1. Molly has **2** bags of beads. How many beads does Molly have in total? — 16

2. Sam has **5** sets of counters. How many counters does Sam have? — 30

3. Tom has **10** bags of marbles. How many marbles is that in total? — 90

4. Jane has **5** bags of beads. How many beads is that altogether? — 40

5. Jon has **10** sets of counters. How many counters are there altogether? — 60

6. Phil has **5** bags of marbles. How many marbles does Phil have? — 45

7. Sara has **10** bags of beads. How many beads is that in total? — 80

8. Tim has **2** sets of counters. How many counters does he have altogether? — 12

9. Sally has **2** sets of marbles. How many marbles is that? — 18

10. Tom has **5** sets of counters. He adds one more counter to each set. How many counters is that in total? — 35

Section 2   Session 6

A   ANSWER

1	10 × 10	=	100
2	5 × 5	=	25
3	2 × 2	=	4
4	10 × 1	=	10
5	7 × 5	=	35
6	8 × 10	=	80
7	3 × 2	=	6
8	9 × 5	=	45
9	6 × 10	=	60
10	4 × 5	=	20

B   ANSWER

1	× 10 = 70	7
2	× 5 = 20	4
3	× 2 = 14	7
4	× 10 = 50	5
5	× 2 = 8	4
6	× 5 = 15	3
7	× 5 = 10	2
8	× 2 = 6	3
9	× 10 = 80	8
10	× 5 = 25	5

C   ANSWER

1 Maggie has **4p**. Tom has **5** times as much money as Maggie. How much does Tom have?   **20p**

2 Tim has **8p**. Phil has **10** times as much money as Tim. How much does Phil have?   **80p**

3 Paul has **6p**. Sally has twice as much money as Paul. How much does Sally have?   **12p**

4 Tom's mum gives him **50p**. This is **5** times the cost of the pencil. How much is the pencil?   **10p**

5 Jan's mum gives her **80p**. This is **10** times the cost of a chew. How much is a chew?   **8p**

6 Paul's mum gives him **18p**. This is twice as much as the cost of a lolly. How much is a lolly?   **9p**

7 Tim buys **5** oranges at **9p** each. How much do the oranges cost altogether?   **45p**

8 Sara buys **10** apples at **4p** each. How much do the apples cost in total?   **40p**

9 Julie buys **2** bananas at **8p** each. What is the total cost?   **16p**

10 Tina buys **2** pears at **6p** each. How much change does she get from **20p**?   **8p**

Section 2   Session 7

A

		ANSWER
1	$15 \div 5 =$	3
2	$18 \div 2 =$	9
3	$30 \div 10 =$	3
4	$40 \div 5 =$	8
5	$40 \div 10 =$	4
6	$12 \div 2 =$	6
7	Double **16** is	32
8	Double **18** is	36
9	Double **19** is	38
10	Double **17** is	34

B

		ANSWER
1	What is **15** divided by **5**?	3
2	What is **30** divided by **10**?	3
3	What is **50** divided by **10**?	5
4	What is **18** divided by **2**?	9
5	What is **45** divided by **5**?	9
6	What is **100** divided by **10**?	10
7	Double thirteen is	twenty-six
8	Double fifteen is	thirty
9	Double eleven is	twenty-two
10	Double fourteen is	twenty-eight

C

		ANSWER
1	Pat shares fifteen grapes between **5** plates. How many grapes are on each plate?	3
2	Paul shares **£30** between **5** people. How much does each person get?	£6
3	Sam has **18** toffees. She gives half of them to May. How many toffees does Sam have now?	9
4	Sally has **14** pencils. She puts half of them into her pencil case. How many pencils did Sally put into her pencil case?	7
5	Tom has **80** stickers. He sticks them into his album and puts **10** on each page. How many pages does Tom fill with stickers?	8
6	There are **90** cars to be parked. The cars have to go into rows of **10**. How many rows are needed?	9
7	Tom has **20** points. He doubles his score. How many points does he have now?	40
8	Niamh doubled her score. Now she has **36** points. How many points did she have to start with?	18
9	Paul has **£17**. His dad doubles Paul's money. How much money does Paul have now?	£34
10	Sara has **£28** because her mum doubled her money. How much did Sara have before her mum doubled the money?	£14

Section 2 Session 8

A | ANSWER

1	50 ÷ 10	=	5
2	40 ÷ 5	=	8
3	16 ÷ 2	=	8
4	15 ÷ 5	=	3
5	70 ÷ 10	=	7
6	12 ÷ 2	=	6
7	Double 15 is		30
8	Double 20 is		40
9	Double 13 is		26
10	Double 17 is		34

B | ANSWER

1	18 divided by 2 is	9
2	25 divided by 5 is	5
3	60 divided by 10 is	6
4	40 divided by 5 is	8
5	14 divided by 2 is	7
6	100 divided by 10 is	10
7	Double ___ is 28.	14
8	Double ___ is 22.	11
9	Double ___ is 36.	18
10	Double ___ is 26.	13

C | ANSWER

Share

1	the marbles between 5 people.	6
2	the marbles between 10 people.	3
3	the apples between 2 people.	10
4	the apples between 5 people.	4
5	the apples between 10 people.	2

Tom	15
Bill	18
Sandro	19
Peter	16
Tim	17

Double

6	Tom's score.	30
7	Bill's score.	36
8	Sandro's score.	38
9	Peter's score.	32
10	Tim's score.	34

Section 2   Session 9

Session Focus
Multiplication facts for 2s, 5s and 10s
Sharing

A   ANSWER

1	6 × 2	=	12
2	7 × 5	=	35
3	8 × 10	=	80
4	9 × 5	=	45
5	10 × 5	=	50
6	8 × 10	=	80

7	12 ÷ 2	=	6
8	35 ÷ 5	=	7
9	60 ÷ 10	=	6
10	14 ÷ 2	=	7

B   ANSWER

1	× 5 = 40	8
2	× 2 = 18	9
3	× 10 = 70	7

4	× 5 = 25	5
5	× 2 = 16	8
6	÷ 2 = 10	20
7	÷ 5 = 6	30
8	÷ 10 = 10	100
9	÷ 5 = 9	45
10	÷ 2 = 6	12

C   ANSWER

How much are these worth?

1	five **2p** coins	10p
2	eight **5p** coins	40p
3	seven **10p** coins	70p
4	four **5p** coins	20p
5	six **2p** coins	12p

Share equally

6	**40p** between **5** people.	8p
7	**80p** between **10** people.	8p
8	**35p** between **5** people.	7p
9	**14p** between **2** people.	7p
10	**90p** between **10** people.	9p

Section 2   Session 10

A   ANSWER

1   **5 × 5**   =   25

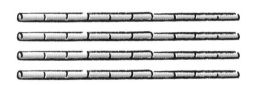

2   **6 × 10**   =   60

3   **2 × 2**   =   4

4   **10 × 5**   =   50

5   **3 × 10**   =   30

6   **4 × 2**   =   8

7   **35 ÷ 5**   =   7

8   **40 ÷ 10**   =   4

9   **10 ÷ 2**   =   5

10 **20 ÷ 5**   =   4

B   ANSWER

1   **7** multiplied by **2** is   14

2   **9** multiplied by **5** is   45

3   **8** multiplied by **10** is   80

4   **5** multiplied by **5** is   25

5   **30** divided by **5** is   6

6   **70** divided by **10** is   7

7   **15** divided by **5** is   3

8   **2** divided by **2** is   1

9   **12** divided by **2** is   6

10 **10** divided by **10** is   1

C   ANSWER

1   How many is **5** multiplied by **10**?   50

2   What is the product of **6** and **5**?   30

3   What is **7** multiplied by **2**?   14

4   What is the product of **3** and **10**?   30

5   How many is **7** multiplied by **5**?   35

6   What is half of **14**?   7

7   What is **8** divided by **2**?   4

8   What is **35** divided by **5**?   7

9   What is **100** divided by **10**?   10

10 What is **50** divided by **5**?   10

Section 2   Check-up 2

Session Focus
Add and subtract mentally. Recall number facts for each number to 10.
Know pairs that total 20. Missing number sequences.
Multiplication facts for 2s, 5s and 10s. Sharing. Doubles to 20.

2   ANSWER

1   $5 + 4$ =   9

2   $9 - 4$ =   5

3   $3 + 3$ =   6

4   $7 + 2$ =   9

5   $8 - 7$ =   1

6   $14 + 9$ =   23

7   $21 + 7$ =   28

8   $32 - 7$ =   25

9   $45 - 5$ =   40

10   $11 + 9$ =   20

11   $20 = 15 +$ ▨   5

12   $20 = 17 +$ ▨   3

13   $20 = 6 +$ ▨   14

14   23, 25, 27, 29, ▨   31

15   32, 34, 36, 38, ▨   40

16   18, 20, 22, 24, ▨   26

17   19, 21, 23, 25, ▨   27

18   6×5 =   30

19   7×10 =   70

20   8×2 =   16

21   4×5 =   20

22   $15 \div 5$ =   3

23   $18 \div 2$ =   9

24   $10 \div 10$ =   1

25   Double **14** is   28

26   Double **18** is   36

27   Double **15** is   30

28   Double **11** is   22

29   Double **16** is   32

30   Double **19** is   38

Section 3 Group record sheet

Class _____

Name	Know pairs that total 20 Session 1	Missing number sequences Session 1	Multiplication facts for 2s, 5s and 10s Session 3	Sharing Session 3	Doubles to 20 Session 5	Halves, quarters and three-quarters of quantities Session 7	Halves, quarters and three-quarters of shapes Session 7

From: **First Mental Arithmetic 5 Answers** by Ann Montague-Smith (ISBN 978 07217 1173 7). Copyright © Schofield & Sims Ltd, 2011. Published by Schofield & Sims Ltd, Dogley Mill, Fenay Bridge, Huddersfield HD8 0NQ, UK (www.schofieldandsims.co.uk). This page may be photocopied for use within your school or institution only.

Section 3 Session 1

Session Focus
Know pairs that total 20
Missing number sequences

A | ANSWER

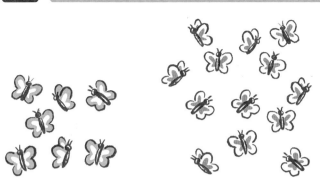

1	13 + 7	=	20
2	3 + ▨ = 20		17
3	7 + ▨ = 20		13
4	▨ + 12 = 20		8
5	▨ + 9 = 20		11
6	▨ + 5 = 20		15
7	16, 17, 18, 19, ▨		20
8	36, 38, 40, ▨		42

9
```
|---|---|---|---|---|---|---|---|---|---|
0   5   10  15  20  25  30  35  40  45  50
```
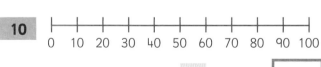

45, 40, 35, ▨ → 30

10
```
|---|---|---|---|---|---|---|---|---|---|
0  10  20  30  40  50  60  70  80  90 100
```

80, 70, 60, 50, ▨ → 40

B | ANSWER

1	4 and ▨ total **20**.	16
2	17 and ▨ total **20**.	3
3	1 and ▨ total **20**.	19

4	**16** and ▨ total **20**.	4
5	▨ and **6** total **20**.	14
6	**7** and ▨ total **20**.	13
7	**12**, **22**, **32**, **42**, ▨	52
8	**46**, **56**, **66**, **76**, ▨	86
9	**99**, **89**, **79**, **69**, ▨	59
10	**67**, **65**, **63**, **61**, ▨	59

C | ANSWER

Write the change from **20p**.

1	Spend **8p**	12p
2	Spend **12p**	8p
3	Spend **15p**	5p
4	Spend **13p**	7p
5	Spend **2p**	18p
6	Spend **16p**	4p
7	**88**, **78**, **68**, **58**, ▨	48
8	**64**, **74**, **84**, **94**, ▨	104
9	**36**, **33**, **30**, **27**, ▨	24
10	**9**, **12**, **15**, **18**, ▨	21

Section 3   Session 2

Session Focus
Know pairs that total 20
Missing number sequences

A   ANSWER

		ANSWER
1	15 + [ ] = 20	5
2	13 + [ ] = 20	7
3	1 + [ ] = 20	19
4	14 + [ ] = 20	6
5	8 + [ ] = 20	12
6	6 + [ ] = 20	14
7	13, 15, 17, 19, [ ]	21
8	18, 20, 22, 24, [ ]	26
9	36, 38, 40, 42, [ ]	44
10	96, 94, 92, 90, [ ]	88

B   ANSWER

		ANSWER
1	12 add [ ] equals 20.	8
2	7 add [ ] equals 20.	13
3	19 add [ ] equals 20.	1
4	[ ] add 12 equals 20.	8
5	[ ] add 14 equals 20.	6
6	[ ] add 18 equals 20.	2
7	36, 46, 56, 66, [ ]	76
8	91, 89, 87, 85, [ ]	83
9	81, 86, 91, 96, [ ]	101
10	12, 17, 22, 27, [ ]	32

C   ANSWER

Apple	6p
Orange	9p
Banana	12p
Pineapple	14p

1   An apple and a

   [pineapple]   cost **20p**

What is the change from **20p** if you buy

2	an apple?	14p
3	a banana?	8p
4	a pineapple?	6p
5	an orange?	11p

Where do you land if you start at

6	7 and count on 5 jumps of 2?	17
7	18 and count on 3 jumps of 5?	33
8	37 and count on 5 jumps of 10?	87
9	42 and count back 3 jumps back of 2?	36
10	58 and count back 4 jumps back of 10?	18

Section 3 Session 3

Session Focus
Multiplication facts for 2s, 5s and 10s
Sharing

A

			ANSWER
1	5 × 2	=	10
2	6 × 2	=	12
3	8 × 5	=	40
4	9 × 10	=	90
5	6 × 5	=	30
6	14 ÷ 2	=	7
7	15 ÷ 5	=	3
8	40 ÷ 10	=	4
9	30 ÷ 5	=	6
10	18 ÷ 2	=	9

B

		ANSWER
1	multiplied by **2** is **14**.	7
2	multiplied by **5** is **35**.	7
3	multiplied by **10** is **50**.	5
4	multiplied by **2** is **18**.	9
5	multiplied by **5** is **45**.	9
6	divided by **5** is **8**.	40
7	divided by **2** is **6**.	12
8	divided by **10** is **2**.	20
9	divided by **5** is **1**.	5
10	**25** divided by is **5**.	5

C

What is the cost of

		ANSWER
1	**8** marbles?	40p
2	**10** chews?	20p
3	**7** tennis balls?	35p
4	**9** apples?	45p
5	**10** oranges?	£1 or 100p

How many does each child receive?

		ANSWER
6	**30** sultanas shared by **5** children	6
7	**40** currants shared by **10** children	4
8	**12** grapes shared by **2** children	6
9	**16** raisins shared by **2** children	8
10	**80** sultanas shared by **10** children	8

Section 3   Session 4

Session Focus
Multiplication facts for 2s, 5s and 10s
Sharing

A   ANSWER

1	8 × 2	=	16
2	9 × 5	=	45
3	7 × 10	=	70
4	4 × 2	=	8
5	7 × 5	=	35
6	12 ÷ 2	=	6
7	40 ÷ 5	=	8
8	40 ÷ 10	=	4
9	16 ÷ 2	=	8
10	25 ÷ 5	=	5

B   ANSWER

1	___ × 5 = 30	6
2	___ × 2 = 20	10
3	___ × 10 = 30	3
4	___ × 5 = 15	3
5	___ × 10 = 100	10
6	___ ÷ 2 = 6	12
7	___ ÷ 5 = 2	10
8	___ ÷ 10 = 7	70
9	___ ÷ 5 = 4	20
10	___ ÷ 10 = 4	40

C   ANSWER

Write how many pieces of fruit altogether.

1	2 bags of apples	12
2	5 bags of apples	30
3	10 bags of apples	60
4	2 bags of bananas	16
5	5 bags of bananas	40
6	10 bags of bananas	80
7	35 pieces of fruit shared between 5	7
8	10 pieces of fruit shared between 10	1
9	50 pieces of fruit shared between 5	10
10	14 pieces of fruit shared between 2	7

Section 3   Session 5

Session Focus
Multiplication facts for 2s, 5s and 10s
Sharing
Doubles to 20

A   ANSWER

1	9×2	=	18
2	10×5	=	50
3	9×10	=	90
4	$45 \div 5$	=	9
5	$60 \div 10$	=	6
6	$8 \div 2$	=	4
7	Double **14** is		28
8	Double **17** is		34
9	Double **19** is		38
10	Double **11** is		22

B   ANSWER

1	**2** lots of **13** is	26
2	**2** lots of **15** is	30
3	**2** lots of **18** is	36
4	**2** lots of **16** is	32
5	**6** multiplied by **5** is	30
6	**7** multiplied by **10** is	70
7	**9** multiplied by **2** is	18
8	**35** divided by **5** is	7
9	**30** divided by **10** is	3
10	**16** divided by **2** is	8

C   ANSWER

How much is

1	double **£18**?	£36
2	double **£12**?	£24
3	double **£13**?	£26

Share equally

4	**£14** between **2**.	£7
5	**£6** between **2**.	£3
6	**£20** between **5**.	£4
7	**£80** between **10**.	£8

How many oranges in

8	**5** packs?	35
9	**2** packs?	14
10	**10** packs?	70

Section 3 Session 6

Session Focus
Multiplication facts for 2s, 5s and 10s
Sharing
Doubles to 20

A

			ANSWER
1	Double **17** is		34
2	Double **13** is		26
3	Double **16** is		32
4	Double **19** is		38
5	**14 ÷ 2**	=	7
6	**25 ÷ 5**	=	5
7	**80 ÷ 10**	=	8
8	**4 × 2**	=	8
9	**8 × 5**	=	40
10	**6 × 10**	=	60

B

		ANSWER
1	**2** lots of **14** is	28
2	Double ___ is **32**.	16
3	Double ___ is **30**.	15
4	**2** lots of **17** is	34
5	**9** multiplied by **2** is	18
6	**8** multiplied by **5** is	40
7	**7** multiplied by **10** is	70
8	**14** shared by **2** is	7
9	**35** shared by **5** is	7
10	**30** shared by **10** is	3

C

Tom	
Bill	16
Mario	18
Sam	15
	19

		ANSWER
1	Double the largest score.	38
2	Double the smallest score.	30
3	Double Tom's score.	32
4	Double Bill's score.	36

How many cakes in total?

5	**10** boxes of **5** cakes	50
6	**8** boxes of **2** cakes	16
7	**10** boxes of **10** cakes	100

8	Share **50** marbles between **5**.	10
9	Share **50** marbles between **10**.	5
10	Share **16** marbles between **2**.	8

Section 3   Session 7

Session Focus
Halves, quarters and three-quarters of quantities
Halves, quarters and three-quarters of shapes

A   ANSWER

Draw a line to show half.

1

2

3

4

5

6	Half of **16** is	8
7	Half of **20** is	10
8	Half of **30** is	15
9	Half of **22** is	11
10	Half of **28** is	14

B   ANSWER

1	A quarter of **12** is	3
2	A quarter of **16** is	4
3	A quarter of **20** is	5
4	Three-quarters of **12** is	9
5	Three-quarters of **16** is	12
6	Three-quarters of **20** is	15

7 Shade a quarter.

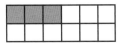

8 Shade a quarter.

9 Shade three-quarters.

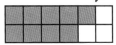

10 Shade three-quarters.

C   ANSWER

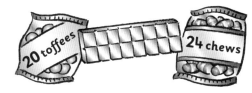

Write how much they eat.

1	Tim eats half of the chocolate.	8	squares
2	Pam eats a quarter of the chocolate.	4	squares
3	Paul eats three-quarters of the chocolate.	12	squares
4	Sally eats half of the toffees.	10	
5	Mary eats a quarter of the toffees.	5	
6	Sara eats three-quarters of the toffees.	15	
7	Toni eats half of the chews.	12	
8	Jamil eats a quarter of the chews.	6	
9	Maisie eats three-quarters of the chews.	18	
10	Tom eats half of the toffees and three-quarters of the chews.	28	

Section 3   Session 8

Session Focus
Halves, quarters and three-quarters of quantities
Halves, quarters and three-quarters of shapes

A ANSWER

Draw a line to show half.

1

2

Draw lines to show a quarter.

3

4

Shade half.

5

6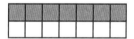

7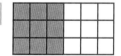

8

9

10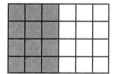

B ANSWER

Shade a quarter.

1

2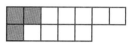

3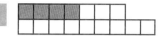

What is

4 a quarter of **20**? | 5 |

5 a quarter of **16**? | 4 |

6 a quarter of **12**? | 3 |

7 three-quarters of **16**? | 12 |

8 three-quarters of **12**? | 9 |

9 three-quarters of **20**? | 15 |

10 three-quarters of **40**? | 30 |

C ANSWER

Draw lines to show three quarters of the shapes.
Shade three-quarters.

1

2

3

What is

4 a quarter of **20**? | 5 |

5 three-quarters of **20**? | 15 |

6 a quarter of **24**? | 6 |

7 three-quarters of **24**? | 18 |

8 a quarter of **32**? | 8 |

9 three-quarters of **32**? | 24 |

10 three-quarters of **28**? | 21 |

Section 3   Session 9

A   ANSWER

1	8 × 5	=	40
2	9 × 2	=	18

3	4 × 10	=	40
4	6 × 5	=	30
5	7 × 10	=	70

6	50 ÷ 10	=	5
7	40 ÷ 5	=	8
8	20 ÷ 2	=	10

9	16 ÷ 2	=	8

10	30 ÷ 5	=	6

B   ANSWER

What is

1	**9** multiplied by **5**?	45
2	**8** multiplied by **2**?	16
3	**7** multiplied by **5**?	35
4	**4** multiplied by **10**?	40
5	**6** multiplied by **2**?	12
6	**40** divided by **5**?	8
7	**90** divided by **10**?	9
8	**30** divided by **5**?	6
9	**16** divided by **2**?	8
10	**100** divided by **10**?	10

C   ANSWER

1	divided by **5** equals **5**.	25
2	divided by **10** equals **6**.	60
3	divided by **2** equals **2**.	4
4	divided by **5** equals **4**.	20
5	divided by **2** equals **9**.	18
6	multiplied by **2** equals **14**.	7
7	multiplied by **5** equals **50**.	10
8	multiplied by **10** equals **100**.	10
9	multiplied by **2** equals **2**.	1
10	multiplied by **5** equals **35**.	7

Section 3 Session 10

A   ANSWER

1	4 × 5	=	20
2	7 × 2	=	14
3	8 × 10	=	80
4	14 ÷ 2	=	7
5	30 ÷ 5	=	6
6	30 ÷ 10	=	3
7	Double 16		32
8	Double 18		36
9	Double 13		26
10	Double 19		38

B   ANSWER

What is the product of

1	8 and 2?	16
2	10 and 10?	100
3	3 and 5?	15

Share equally

4	45 between 5.	9
5	60 between 10.	6
6	18 between 2.	9
7	Double 14 is	28
8	Double 18 is	36
9	Double 13 is	26
10	Double 12 is	24

C   ANSWER

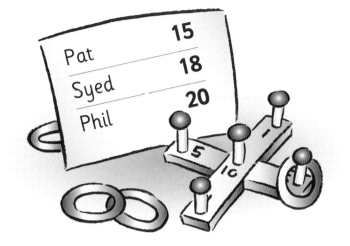

Pat 15
Syed 18
Phil 20

1	Double Pat's score	30
2	Double Syed's score	36
3	Double Phil's score	40
4	Divide Pat's score by 5	3
5	Divide Syed's score by 2	9
6	Divide Phil's score by 10	2

How many eggs in

7	2 boxes?	16
8	5 boxes?	40
9	10 boxes?	80
10	Double the eggs in one box and take 6 eggs away.	10

38

Section 3 Check-up 3

Session Focus
Know pairs that total 20 Missing number sequences. Multiplication facts for 2s, 5s and 10s. Sharing. Doubles to 20. Halves, quarters and three-quarters of quantities. Halves, quarters and three-quarters of shapes.

3   ANSWER

1	___ + 5 = 20		15
2	___ + 14 = 20		6
3	12 + ___ = 20		8
4	93, 92, 91, 90, ___		89
5	82, 84, 86, 88, ___		90
6	6, 11, 16, 21, ___		26
7	5×5	=	25
8	9×10	=	90
9	7×5	=	35
10	2×2	=	4
11	$12 \div 2$	=	6
12	$15 \div 5$	=	3
13	$40 \div 10$	=	4
14	$45 \div 5$	=	9
15	Double **13**		26
16	Double **17**		34
17	Double **11**		22
18	Double **20**		40

19 Shade half of this shape.

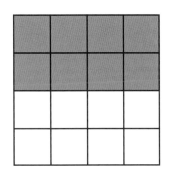

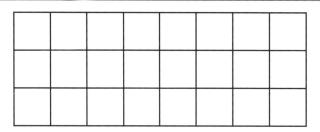

20	What is half of **24**?	12
21	What is a quarter of **24**?	6
22	What is three-quarters of **24**?	18

23 Shade a quarter of this shape.

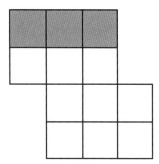

24	How many squares need to be shaded to show three-quarters of the shape above?	9
25	Double **18** and add **2**.	38
26	Double **17** and add **6**.	40

27	The product of **3** and **5**.	15
28	The product of **6** and **10**.	60
29	Share **40** sultanas equally between **5**.	8
30	Share **12** apples equally between **2**.	6

Check-up 4
Measures, Shape and space, Handling data

Session Focus
Recognise 3D shapes from drawings. Recognise line symmetry.
Block graphs. Sort onto a diagram. Reading scales. Choose appropriate units
of length. Time: quarter to and quarter past. Digital clock time in quarter hours.
Whole, half and quarter turns.

ANSWER

1   **2**

3

1	Which shape is a cube?	1
2	Which shape is a cone?	3
3	Which shape is a cuboid?	2

4 Draw the line of symmetry.

5 Draw a line of symmetry.

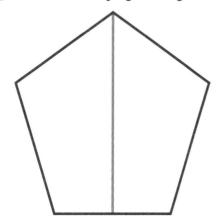

6 Sort the numbers from **1** to **20** onto the diagram.

	2-digit numbers	Not **2**-digit numbers
Odd	11 13 15 17 19	1 3 5 7 9
Not odd	10 12 14 16 18 20	2 4 6 8

7 What is the next odd number after **20**?   21

8 What is the next not-odd number after **20**?   22

Answer the questions about this block graph.

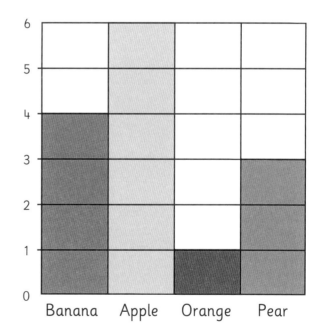

9 Which is the favourite fruit?   apple

10 Which fruit do the children like least?   orange

40

11 How many more children like apples than pears? | 3

12 How many children voted for their favourite fruit? | 14

20   **22**   **29**   30

13 Write the number **22** on the scale.

14 Write the number **29** on the scale.

15 What unit of length would you choose to measure the height of an elephant?

| metres |

16 What unit of length would you choose to measure the height of a mouse?

| centimetres |

17 What unit of length would you choose to measure your height?

| centimetres |

18 How many minutes in one hour? | 60

Draw the hand on the clocks to show the times.

19 **6.15**

20 **8.45**

21 **12.00**

Write whole, half or quarter turn as your answer.

22 How far has the door turned?

| quarter turn |

41

23 How far has the child turned?

half turn

24 How far have the sails of the windmill turned?

whole turn

25 How many hours difference is there?

2

26 Draw hands to show the time in **15** minutes.

27 Write the same time on the digital clock.

7 : 45

28 John has **18** metres of rope. He cuts the rope in half. How long is each piece?

9m

29 The bus journey took **15** minutes. It is now **6.30**. What time did the journey start?

6.15

30 A bag of flour weighs **2kg**. How much would **5** bags of flour weigh?

10kg

Just facts

0 + 20	=	20
1 + 19	=	20
2 + 18	=	20
3 + 17	=	20
4 + 16	=	20
5 + 15	=	20
6 + 14	=	20
7 + 13	=	20
8 + 12	=	20
9 + 11	=	20
10 + 10	=	20
11 + 9	=	20
12 + 8	=	20
13 + 7	=	20
14 + 6	=	20
15 + 5	=	20
16 + 4	=	20
17 + 3	=	20
18 + 2	=	20
19 + 1	=	20
20 + 0	=	20

1 + 1	=	2
2 + 2	=	4
3 + 3	=	6
4 + 4	=	8
5 + 5	=	10
6 + 6	=	12
7 + 7	=	14
8 + 8	=	16
9 + 9	=	18
10 + 10	=	20
11 + 11	=	22
12 + 12	=	24
13 + 13	=	26
14 + 14	=	28
15 + 15	=	30
16 + 16	=	32
17 + 17	=	34
18 + 18	=	36
19 + 19	=	38
20 + 20	=	40

Just facts

0 + 0	=	0	0 + 1	=	1	0 + 2	=	2
1 + 0	=	1	1 + 1	=	2	1 + 2	=	3
2 + 0	=	2	2 + 1	=	3	2 + 2	=	4
3 + 0	=	3	3 + 1	=	4	3 + 2	=	5
4 + 0	=	4	4 + 1	=	5	4 + 2	=	6
5 + 0	=	5	5 + 1	=	6	5 + 2	=	7
6 + 0	=	6	6 + 1	=	7	6 + 2	=	8
7 + 0	=	7	7 + 1	=	8	7 + 2	=	9
8 + 0	=	8	8 + 1	=	9	8 + 2	=	10
9 + 0	=	9	9 + 1	=	10	9 + 2	=	11
10 + 0	=	10	10 + 1	=	11	10 + 2	=	12

0 + 3	=	3	0 + 4	=	4	0 + 5	=	5
1 + 3	=	4	1 + 4	=	5	1 + 5	=	6
2 + 3	=	5	2 + 4	=	6	2 + 5	=	7
3 + 3	=	6	3 + 4	=	7	3 + 5	=	8
4 + 3	=	7	4 + 4	=	8	4 + 5	=	9
5 + 3	=	8	5 + 4	=	9	5 + 5	=	10
6 + 3	=	9	6 + 4	=	10	6 + 5	=	11
7 + 3	=	10	7 + 4	=	11	7 + 5	=	12
8 + 3	=	11	8 + 4	=	12	8 + 5	=	13
9 + 3	=	12	9 + 4	=	13	9 + 5	=	14
10 + 3	=	13	10 + 4	=	14	10 + 5	=	15

Just facts

0 + 6	=	6	0 + 7	=	7	0 + 8	=	8
1 + 6	=	7	1 + 7	=	8	1 + 8	=	9
2 + 6	=	8	2 + 7	=	9	2 + 8	=	10
3 + 6	=	9	3 + 7	=	10	3 + 8	=	11
4 + 6	=	10	4 + 7	=	11	4 + 8	=	12
5 + 6	=	11	5 + 7	=	12	5 + 8	=	13
6 + 6	=	12	6 + 7	=	13	6 + 8	=	14
7 + 6	=	13	7 + 7	=	14	7 + 8	=	15
8 + 6	=	14	8 + 7	=	15	8 + 8	=	16
9 + 6	=	15	9 + 7	=	16	9 + 8	=	17
10 + 6	=	16	10 + 7	=	17	10 + 8	=	18

0 + 9	=	9	0 + 10	=	10
1 + 9	=	10	1 + 10	=	11
2 + 9	=	11	2 + 10	=	12
3 + 9	=	12	3 + 10	=	13
4 + 9	=	13	4 + 10	=	14
5 + 9	=	14	5 + 10	=	15
6 + 9	=	15	6 + 10	=	16
7 + 9	=	16	7 + 10	=	17
8 + 9	=	17	8 + 10	=	18
9 + 9	=	18	9 + 10	=	19
10 + 9	=	19	10 + 10	=	20

Just facts

Multiplication facts for 2s

1 × 2 = | 2 |

2 × 2 = | 4 |

3 × 2 = | 6 |

4 × 2 = | 8 |

5 × 2 = | 10 |

6 × 2 = | 12 |

7 × 2 = | 14 |

8 × 2 = | 16 |

9 × 2 = | 18 |

10 × 2 = | 20 |

Multiplication facts for 5s

1 × 5 = | 5 |

2 × 5 = | 10 |

3 × 5 = | 15 |

4 × 5 = | 20 |

5 × 5 = | 25 |

6 × 5 = | 30 |

7 × 5 = | 35 |

8 × 5 = | 40 |

9 × 5 = | 45 |

10 × 5 = | 50 |

Multiplication facts for 10s

1 × 10 = | 10 |

2 × 10 = | 20 |

3 × 10 = | 30 |

4 × 10 = | 40 |

5 × 10 = | 50 |

6 × 10 = | 60 |

7 × 10 = | 70 |

8 × 10 = | 80 |

9 × 10 = | 90 |

10 × 10 = | 100 |

Just facts

Division facts for 2s

$2 \div 2$ = 1

$4 \div 2$ = 2

$6 \div 2$ = 3

$8 \div 2$ = 4

$10 \div 2$ = 5

$12 \div 2$ = 6

$14 \div 2$ = 7

$16 \div 2$ = 8

$18 \div 2$ = 9

$20 \div 2$ = 10

Division facts for 5s

$5 \div 5$ = 1

$10 \div 5$ = 2

$15 \div 5$ = 3

$20 \div 5$ = 4

$25 \div 5$ = 5

$30 \div 5$ = 6

$35 \div 5$ = 7

$40 \div 5$ = 8

$45 \div 5$ = 9

$50 \div 5$ = 10

Division facts for 10s

$10 \div 10$ = 1

$20 \div 10$ = 2

$30 \div 10$ = 3

$40 \div 10$ = 4

$50 \div 10$ = 5

$60 \div 10$ = 6

$70 \div 10$ = 7

$80 \div 10$ = 8

$90 \div 10$ = 9

$100 \div 10$ = 10

Full list of the Schofield & Sims First Mental Arithmetic books

Workbooks

First Mental Arithmetic 1	ISBN 978 07217 1163 8
First Mental Arithmetic 2	ISBN 978 07217 1164 5
First Mental Arithmetic 3	ISBN 978 07217 1165 2
First Mental Arithmetic 4	ISBN 978 07217 1166 9
First Mental Arithmetic 5	ISBN 978 07217 1167 6
First Mental Arithmetic 6	ISBN 978 07217 1168 3

Answers

First Mental Arithmetic 1 Answers	ISBN 978 07217 1169 0
First Mental Arithmetic 2 Answers	ISBN 978 07217 1170 6
First Mental Arithmetic 3 Answers	ISBN 978 07217 1171 3
First Mental Arithmetic 4 Answers	ISBN 978 07217 1172 0
First Mental Arithmetic 5 Answers	ISBN 978 07217 1173 7
First Mental Arithmetic 6 Answers	ISBN 978 07217 1174 4

Related materials

The **I can do** teaching method was devised for use at Key Stage 2, with **Schofield & Sims Mental Arithmetic**, and has achieved outstanding results.

This teaching method is equally suitable for use at Key Stage 1, with **First Mental Arithmetic**.

To find out more, watch the film **'I can do maths' in practice** online at **www.schofieldandsims.co.uk/icando/** and order the **I can do maths** Teacher's Guide.

I can do maths Teacher's Guide	ISBN 978 07217 1115 7

All available from

Schofield & Sims Ltd, Dogley Mill, Fenay Bridge, Huddersfield HD8 0NQ

www.schofieldandsims.co.uk

E-mail: sales@schofieldandsims.co.uk
Phone: 01484 607080 Facsimile: 01484 606815